COLLECTOR'S GUIDE TO
OAK
FURNITURE

JENNIFER GEORGE

COLLECTOR BOOKS
A Division of Schroeder Publishing Co., Inc.

Searching For A Publisher?

We are always looking for knowledgeable people considered to be experts within their fields. If you feel that there is a real need for a book on your collectible subject and have a large comprehensive collection, contact us.

Collector Books
P.O. Box 3009
Paducah, Kentucky 42002-3009

Cover design by Beth Summers
Book design by Terri Stalions

Additional copies of this book may be ordered from:

Collector Books
P.O. Box 3009
Paducah, Kentucky 42002-3009

@$12.95. Add $2.00 for postage and handling.

Printed by IMAGE GRAPHICS, INC., Paducah, Kentucky

Contents

Chapter One: Sampling of Prices of Oak Furniture 7

Chapter Two: Auction Prices 11

Chapter Three: Combination Bookcase-Desks 14

Chapter Four: Kitchen Cabinets 33

Chapter Five: Pressed Backs 47

Chapter Six: Representative Oak Furniture 61
- Bed and bedroom set 62
- Bookcase 64
- Chiffonier 67
- Chifforobe 69
- Children's examples 70
- China buffet 72
- China cabinet 74
- Commode 76
- Corner cupboard 78
- Cupboard 79
- Desk 82
- Dining table 86
- Dresser 88
- File cabinet 91
- Hall tree 92
- Hanging examples 94
- Ice box 96
- Lady's desk 97
- Library table 99
- Occupational examples 100
- Parlor table 103
- Phonograph 105
- Plant stand 108
- Princess dresser 109
- Rocker 112
- Server 114
- Sideboard 115
- Sofa 118
- Stickley 119
- Taboret 120
- Umbrella stand 121
- Vanity 122
- Wardrobe 125

Preface

In this book, the author has selected three articles of oak furniture for special emphasis. The major article, with 21 photographs, shows construction features and styles in combination bookcase-desks. The minor emphasis, with 14 photographs, deals with Hoosier and Hoosier-type cabinets in which the author pictures a selection of these kitchen cabinets produced by different companies as well as the Hoosier Company itself. Fifteen pressed back chairs and rockers are featured in the third section. The concluding chapter pictures over 90 other representative pieces of oak furniture.

The price under each photograph has been set by the owners. Because prices in various geographical areas often differ, each photograph is identified by the shop's name where it was taken. Some pictures secured in private homes are identified by the words *Private Collector* in order to protect the anonymity of the collector.

With Thanks

The author expresses her thanks to the following people who provided information and pictures for this book.

Illinois

Heartland Antique Mall
Geneseo

Hickory Hill Antiques
Galesburg

Illinois Antique Center
Peoria

Pleasant Hill Antique Mall and Tea
    Room
East Peoria

Indiana

Country Shops of Grabill
Grabill

Karen's Antique Mall
Fort Wayne

The Leo Antique Exchange
Leo

Webb's Antique Mall
Centerville

Iowa

Antique America
Davenport

Country Caboose Antiques
West Des Moines

Fifth Street Mall
West Des Moines

Melon City Antique Mart
Muscatine

Ohio

Broadway Antique Mall
Lebanon

Jeffrey's Antique Gallery
Findlay

Miller's Antique Market
Lebanon

Private Collectors

Mary and LeRoy Arp
Ruth Ann Frenell
Mary and Bob Grueskin
Colleen Higgins
Linda Hoeffing
Barbara and Ted Lafferty
Cindy and David Van Lendegen

Chapter One

A Sampling of Prices of Oak Furniture

(As seen in shops and at shows during my travels)

Barber backbar	$3,500.00; $6,500.00
Beds	$175.00; $335.00; $395.00; $450.00; $495.00; $525.00; $545.00; $550.00; $995.00
Bedroom set (three piece)	$1,150.00; $1,250.00; $1,500.00; $3,200.00; $3,495.00; $3,850.00
Bedroom set (two piece)	$975.00; $1,175.00; $1,295.00; $1,600.00
Bookcase	$295.00; $335.00; $475.00; $495.00; $595.00; $650.00; $675.00; $695.00; $750.00; $850.00; $895.00; $995.00; $1,025.00; $1,125.00; $1,295.00; $2,800.00
Chevalle mirror	$495.00; $975.00
Chiffonier	$310.00; $325.00; $395.00; $425.000; $450.00; $475.00; $495.00; $525.00; $595.00; $625.00; $650.00; $1,495.00
Chifforobe	$245.00; $325.00; $595.00; $795.00
China buffet	$425.00; $475.00; $495.00; $575.00; $900.00; $1,150.00; $1,275.00; $1,595.00; $4,500.00
China buffet (double)	$1,195.00; $1,350.00; $1,595.00
China cabinet	$425.00; $595.00; $650.00; $695.00; $825.00; $850.00; $875.00; $895.00; $975.00; $995.00; $1,100.00; $1,500.00; $1,650.00; $2,250.00; $2,500.00; $2,795.00; $3,900.00

Corner china cabinet	$950.00; $975.00; $1,295.00; $1,495.00; $2,400.00; $2,600.00
Clocks (kitchen)	$175.00; $215.00; $225.00; $325.00; $350.00
Clocks (wall)	$295.00; $325.00; $345.00; $395.00; $425.00; $450.00; $495.00; $1,650.00
Commode	$160.00; $225.00; $285.00; $295.00; $310.00; $325.00; $330.00; $340.000; $355.000; $365.00; $385.00; $410.00; $415.00; $425.00; $475.00; $485.00; $495.00; $550.000
Couch	$290.00; $425.00; $525.00; $575.00; $650.00

Desk

Combination bookcase	$575.00; $625.00; $725.00; $795.00; $825.00; $850.00; $875.00; $895.00; $925.00; $995.00; $1,095.00; $1,150.00; $1,295.00; $1,325.00; $1,425.00; $1,750.00; $2,650.00
Cylinder desk	$1,475.00; $1,495.00; $2,000.00
Cylinder secretary	$1,500.00; $2,295.00; $2,900.00; $3,485.00
Double combination	$1,325.00; $1,650.00; $2,250.00
Fall front desk	$425.00; $495.00; $525.00; $595.00; $625.00; $650.00; $675.00; $725.00; $795.00; $1,300.00
Fall front secretary	$995.00; $1,085.00; $1,295.00; $1,350.00; $1,425.00; $1,495.00; $1,600.00; $1,685.00; $1,995.00
Lady's	$335.00; $395.00; $445.00; $495.00; $525.00; $550.00; $620.00; $725.00; $795.00; $850.00; $1,300.00
Mission fall front	$495.00; $595.00; $695.00
Roll top	$1,450.00; $1,495.00; $1,500.00; $1,725.00
Sheboygan	$1,295.00; $1,695.00

Dresser	$350.00; $395.00; $425.00; $450.00; $475.00; $495.00; $565.00; $675.00
Chevalle	$495.00; $525.00; $595.00; $665.00
Princess	$310.00; $350.00; $375.00; $395.00; $425.00; $990.00
File cabinet	$425.00; $495.00; $525.00; $695.00
Hall mirror	$175.00; $250.00; $275.00; $325.00; $350.00
Hall tree	$525.00; $585.00; $650.00; $795.00; $875.00; $895.00; $950.00; $995.00; $1,095.00; $1,190.00; $1,250.00; $1,295.00; $1,695.00; $1,750.00; $1,795.00; $2,495.00; $3,500.00
Hall tree (double)	$1,195.00; $1,295.00
Highchair	$165.00; $195.00; $225.00; $245.00; $275.00; $315.00
Combination	$395.00; $425.00; $450.00; $495.00
Ice box	$345.00; $425.00; $475.00; $485.00; $495.00; $595.00; $695.00; $750.00
Kitchen cabinet	$475.00; $595.00; $695.00; $725.00; $750.00; $795.00; $850.00; $895.00; $950.00; $1,295.00
Kitchen Hoosier	$495.00; $595.00; $625.00; $650.00; $695.00; $725.00; $795.00; $895.00; $950.00; $995.00; $1,350.00
Medicine cabinet	$165.00; $225.00; $275.00
Morris chair	$225.00; $250.00; $275.00; $595.00
Music cabinet	$165.00; $290.00; $395.00; $400.00
Parlor set	
Two piece	$365.00
Three piece	$300.00; $595.00
Pedestal	$125.00; $135.00; $145.00; $155.00

Piano stool $110.00; $135.00; $165.00

Rocker
  Children's $165.00; $245.00

  Common $165.00; $210.00; $245.00; $265.00; $310.00; $345.00;
                 $395.00; $450.00; $485.00; $595.00

  Platform $195.00; $219.00; $310.00; $325.00; $375.00; $500.00

  Sewing $165.00; $185.00

Roman chair $235.00; $345.00; $650.00

Sideboard $495.00; $525.00; $650.00; $695.00; $750.00; $795.00;
                 $800.00; $895.00; $995.00; $1,095.00; $1,250.00;
                 $1,295.00; $1,385.00; $1,475.00; $1,800.00; $1,975.00;
                 $1,995.00

Stack bookcase $350.00; $495.00; $515.00; $595.00; $600.00; $650.00;
                 $750.00; $795.00; $825.00; $895.00

Swivel chair $145.00; $360.00

Table
  Library $135.00; $275.00; $325.00; $465.00; $475.00; $495.00;
                 $525.00; $550.00; $725.00; $850.00

  Parlor $125.00; $145.00; $165.00; $245.00; $250.00; $255.00;
                 $275.00; $325.00; $350.00; $375.00; $400.00; $525.00

  Pedestal $150.00; $450.00; $650.00

  Round $895.00; $950.00; $1,450.00; $1,995.00

  Square $325.00; $495.00; $525.00; $550.00; $850.00; $895.00;
                 $995.00; $1,295.00

Umbrella stand $110.00; $125.00; $145.00

Vanity $425.00; $445.00; $465.00; $550.00

Wardrobe $665.00; $795.00; $895.00; $995.00; $1,195.00; $1,250.00;
                 $1,495.00; $1,595.00; $2,500.00

Chapter Two

Auction Prices

The auction prices listed in this section are arranged alphabetically by: Bedroom, Dining Room, Hall Entry, Kitchen, Library, and Parlor. Mission is listed at the end of the furniture section. Because these prices were secured from various antique journals and were not personally seen, only generic names are used rather than descriptive entries for the types of furniture listed.

Bedroom

Bed

Iowa	$150.00 – 810.00
Nebraska	$270.00
Texas	$325.00 – 550.00
Wyoming	$600.00

Bedroom Set (three pieces)

Iowa	$1,010.00 – 1,650.00
Nebraska	$1,700.00
Texas	$1,200.00 – 2,000.00

Chevalle dresser

Iowa	$325.00
Nebraska	$450.00
Texas	$400.00

Commode

Iowa	$150.00 – 275.00
Minnesota	$220.00
Missouri	$150.00
Wisconsin	$235.00

Dresser

Illinois	$230.00
Iowa	$160.00 – 425.00
Kansas	$210.00
Texas	$200.00 – 375.00
Wyoming	$170.00 – 290.00

Highboy (Chiffonier)

Iowa	$155.00 – 500.00
Texas	$350.00
Wyoming	$310.00

Wardrobe

Iowa	$500.00 – 810.00
Kansas	$350.00
Texas	$300.00 – 550.00
Wyoming	$225.00

Dining Room

Buffet/Sideboard

Iowa	$230.00 – 1,100.00
Kansas	$320.00 – 395.00
Minnesota	$1,025.00
Nebraska	$440.00 – 460.00
Texas	$387.00

China cabinet

Iowa	$450.00 – 2,100.00
Kansas	$425.00 – 1,000.00
Louisiana	$1,750.00
Minnesota	$770.00
Missouri	$475.00
Nebraska	$875.00 – 2,850.00
New York	$1,320.00

Texas $725.00 – 1,250.00
Wyoming $900.00 – 950.00

Pressed back chair
Iowa $65.00 – 70.00 ea.
Minnesota $70.00 – 135.00 ea.

Tables (round)
Illinois $300.00
Iowa $350.00 – 1,650.00
Kansas $430.00 – 575.00
Nebraska $290.00 – 350.00
Wyoming $500.00

Tables (square)
Iowa $210.00 – 540.00
Nebraska $250.00
Texas $535.00

Hall Entry

Hall tree
Illinois $640.00
Iowa $850.00
Kansas $385.00
Missouri $685.00
Texas $360.00 – 1,500.00

Kitchen

Hawkeye Cupboard
Iowa $900.00 – 1,025.00

Hoosier type cupboard
California $675.00
Iowa $385.00 – 1,300.00
Kansas $310.00
Minnesota $325.00 – 525.00
Nebraska $380.00 – 480.00

Ice box
Illinois $300.00
Iowa $310.00 – 600.00
Kansas $385.00
Minnesota $235.00 – 430.00

Stepback cupboard
Iowa $420.00 – 950.00
Minnesota $685.00
Nebraska $460.00 – 700.00
Texas $700.00

Wall telephone
Iowa $130.00 – 190.00
Kansas $160.00
Nebraska $160.00
Texas $150.00

Library

Bookcase
Iowa $275.00 – 600.00
Nebraska $650.00 – 1,100.00
Texas $275.00 – 600.00
Wyoming $450.00

Combination bookcase/desk
Illinois $600.00 – 625.00
Iowa $480.00 – 950.00
Kansas $1,200.00
Minnesota $330.00
Nebraska $525.00 – 700.00
Texas $575.00 – 1,000.00
Wyoming $900.00

Fall front secretary
Missouri $1,250.00

Lady's desk
Iowa $250.00 – 400.00
Kansas $525.00
Minnesota $450.00
Missouri $620.00

Larkin drop front
Texas $225.00 – 350.00

Library table
Iowa $140.00 – 175.00
Kansas $145.00
Nebraska $160.00

Roll top desk
Iowa	$750.00 – 1,100.00
Missouri	$410.00
Texas	$800.00 – 1,200.00

Stack bookcase
Iowa	$265.00 – 570.00
Kansas	$280.00 – 400.00
Nebraska	$385.00 – 525.00
Texas	$300.00

Parlor

Parlor table
Iowa	$80.00 – 380.00
Texas	$70.00 – 375.00

Parlor sets (three pieces)
Nebraska	$1,000.00
Texas	$450.00

Platform rocker
Iowa	$150.00 – 200.00
Kansas	$130.00
Texas	$150.00

Pressed back rocker
Iowa	$150.00 – 290.00
Minnesota	$135.00
Texas	$175.00

Pump organ
Iowa	$325.00
Nebraska	$425.00

Mission Style Furniture

Those articles marked with an asterisk were auctioned in Illinois. The others were auctioned in California. Makers are listed in italics.

Harden
Bookcase	$1,150.00

Lifetime
China cabinet	$850.00

Limbert
Center table, 36"	$550.00
Octagonal table	$1,800.00

Stickley Brothers
Nightstand (one drawer)	$900.00
Lamp table	$725.00

Stickley, Gustav
*Bookcase	$20,900.00
Footstool #300	$1,150.00
Library table, 54"	$1,650.00
Music cabinet (one door)	$3,100.00
V back armchairs (pair)	$1,000.00
V back rocker	$500.00
Umbrella stand	$450.00

Stickley, L. & J.G.
China cabinet	$2,500.00
*Crib settle #223	$12,100.00
Sideboard	$1,100.00

Chapter Three

Combination Bookcase-Desk

Combination Bookcase-Desk

The name *combination bookcase-desk* appeared in early twentieth-century mail order catalogues to describe a unit that combined both a desk and a bookcase. Other names, such as *combination bookcase and writing desk, combination bookcase desk* or *library case,* and *secretary* were also descriptive titles. Today, *secretary, side-by-side,* or *combination desk* are commonly used terms to describe these pieces.

This drop lid desk with its attached bookcase had three major divisions. The predominant one is the right-handed desk with the glass enclosed shelf area to the left of the drop-lid section.

The second category has the drop lid in the middle between two bookcases. This design makes research materials easily available to both left and right-handers. Such bookcases are not as common as the desks with the single storage unit.

A desk situated to the left of the book shelves is seldom seen in the early catalogs or currently, for that matter, in antique shops nationally. As a consequence, this type may be more expensive to purchase.

Pigeon holes and small drawers inside the drop lid section help in the organization of papers, and provide storage for stationery and other writing materials including ink bottles.

The doors on bookcases have either straight, concave or convex glass panels. These latter two examples were called "bent" or "swell" glass in the early furniture catalogues. Sometimes an 'S' bend is seen. Other features include adjustable shelves and casters for mobility.

The section under the drop lid sometimes included a series of drawers with the top one bowed and projecting over the others. Serpentine types result when the drawer's surface curves in and out. However, many of the sections under the drop lid have a cupboard door instead of drawers. On the less expensive versions, the base shelves are open or covered with a cloth curtain.

Brass handles were popular. Generally they were the bail type with pressed brass plates forming an infinite selection of designs. Other drawer pulls included the less decorative bail pull without a back plate or the infrequently used wooden handles.

Although golden oak was perhaps the most popular finish, some companies provided a dark, fumed oak finish.

Plate 1. *Combination bookcase-desk with applied decorations and bail handles; 39" wide, 13" deep, 58" high. Karen's Antique Mall. $895.00.*

Plate 2*. Combination bookcase-desk with incised decorations and bail handles; 43" wide, 15" deep, 68" high. Fifth Street Mall. $1,895.00.*

Plate 3. *Combination bookcase-desk with convex glass and bail handles; 36" wide, 12" deep, 74" high. Melon City Antique Mart. $995.00.*

Plate 4. *Combination bookcase-desk with incised decorations and bail handles; 39" wide, 14" deep, 66" high. Webb's Antique Mall. $895.00.*

Plate 5. *Combination bookcase-desk with convex glass, incised decorations and bail handles; 38" wide, 13" deep, 75" high. Webb's Antique Mall. $1,295.00.*

Plate 6. *Combination bookcase-desk with convex glass; 41" wide, 14" deep, 65" high. Jeffrey's Antique Gallery. $485.00.*

Plate 7. Combination bookcase-desk with paw feet and bail handles; 43" wide, 14" deep, 68" high. Illinois Antique Center. $1,500.00.

Plate 8. Combination bookcase-desk with applied decorations and bail handles; 41" wide, 14" deep, 74" high. Fifth Street Mall. $1,250.00.

Plate 9. *Combination bookcase-desk with applied decorations and bail handles, made by Larkin; 38" wide, 13" deep, 64" high. Melon City Antique Mart. $740.00.*

Plate 10. Combination bookcase-desk with convex glass, incised decorations, and bail handles; 38" wide, 12" deep, 72" high. Webb's Antique Mall. $995.00.

Plate 11. Combination bookcase-desk with applied decorations and bail handles; 38" wide, 12" deep, 69" high. Antique America. $696.00.

Plate 12. Combination bookcase-desk with applied decorations; 36" wide, 13" deep, 70" high. Webb's Antique Mall. $745.00.

Plate 13. *Combination bookcase-desk with applied decorations and bail handles; 38" wide, 14" deep, 64" high. Jeffrey's Antique Gallery. $695.00.*

Plate 14. *Combination bookcase-desk with applied and incised decorations and bail handles; 38" wide, 13" deep, 66" high. Country Shops of Grabill. $695.00.*

Plate 15. Combination bookcase-desk with applied decorations and bail handles; 38" wide, 11" deep, 62" high. Jeffrey's Antique Gallery. $550.00.

Plate 16. Combination bookcase-desk with convex glass, applied decorations, bail handles, and leaded glass; 39" wide, 14" deep, 69" high. Illinois Antique Center. $1,150.00.

Plate 17. *Combination bookcase-desk with convex glass, applied decorations, bail handles and leaded glass; 39" wide, 14" deep, 72" high. Illinois Antique Center. $1,150.00.*

Plate 18. *Combination bookcase-desk with convex glass, bail handles and leaded glass; 41" wide, 14" deep, 66" high. Leo Antique Exchange. $1,195.00.*

Plate 19. *Combination bookcase-desk with incised decorations, bail handles, and desk section on the left hand side to accommodate left-handed writers; 41" wide, 13" deep, 68" high. Karen's Antique Mall. $875.00.*

Plate 20. *Combination bookcase-desk with incised and applied decorations, bail handles, and bookcases on each side of the desk section; 55" wide, 11" deep, 75" high. Webb's Antique Mall. $1,495.00.*

Plate 21. *Combination bookcase-desk with incised and brass decorations, and bookcases on each side of the desk section; 56" wide, 14" deep, 70" high. Pleasant Hill Antique Mall. $1,800.00.*

Chapter Four

Kitchen Cabinets

Kitchen Cabinets

Illustrated in this section on Hoosier cabinets are examples made by Sellers, Nappanee, and Hoosier of Indiana, Klauke of Ohio, Wilson of Grand Rapids, Michigan, Hawkeye of Burlington, Iowa and Ariel whose location is unknown.

These two-piece cabinets are often characterized by a base which has a combination of doors and drawers, oftentimes with a pull out cutting board and a work surface of porcelain, zinc or wood that can be pulled out to provide greater space.

Base drawers sometimes were metal lined for storing breads or other baked goods. Sifters, flour bins and sugar containers were frequently a part of these cabinets which were noted for their compactness and roominess.

The top section is often comprised of doors with glass or wooden panels and a tambour pull down door, called either "dust proof roll curtain" or "easy rolling shutter" in some of the early catalogs. These tambours are occasionally seen operating in a horizontal direction.

Because most of these versatile cabinets were made in Indiana, the Hoosier state, these kitchen pieces were dubbed "Hoosiers." The original brand named Hoosier was first made in New Castle, Indiana. Other manufacturers, seeing the popularity of these cabinets made similar examples which are also called "Hoosiers."

Early catalogs, notably Sears and Wards, picture examples of these early kitchen cabinets. Wards were advertised as "Ward Bilt Kitchen Cabinets" or "Master Made Kitchen Cabinets." Golden oak or white enamel were the two most popular finishes available. Their cabinets were 40", 48", and 56" wide. The latter was referred to as "almost a kitchen in itself."

Sears promoted the Wilson Kitchen Cabinet, made in Grand Rapids, Michigan. The Wilson "Leader" cabinet, pictured in a 1921 Sears catalog, was promoted for its special features, including an easily filled 50-pound capacity flour bin with window front and patent sifter; spacious, uncluttered work table with genuine porcelain top; removable bread board; sliding shelf in bottom of cupboard; roll drop curtain; deep bread drawer; strongly braced block for food chopper; swinging sugar jar equipped with patent catch; and a meal bin having a capacity of 20 pounds. These cabinets measured 70" high, 42" wide, and 25" deep with the top work surface pushed in. When open a space of 38 x 42" was available. The one with the metal top sold for $27.85 and the porcelain example could be purchased for $33.85.

Contrast this $33.85 Wilson cabinet from the 1921 catalog with a Wilson cabinet, as shown among the pictures that follow, available in the early 1990s for over $1,400.00.

Plate 22. *Seller's kitchen cabinet made in Elwood, Indiana with pull-down tambour door and porcelain pull-out working surface; 41" wide, 27" deep base, 70" high. Karen's Antique Mall. $795.00.*

Plate 23. *Klauke kitchen cabinet made in Bren, Ohio with side-moving tambour door, pull-out porcelain work surface, and frosted design on door panes; 45" wide, 28" deep base, 75" high. Jeffrey's Antique Gallery. $1,550.00.*

Plate 24. *Wilson kitchen cabinet made in Grand Rapids, Michigan with pull-down tambour door, pull-out porcelain work surface and slag glass; 48" wide, 28" deep base, 72" high. Jeffrey's Antique Gallery. $1,450.00.*

Plate 25. *McDougall kitchen cabinet made in Frankfort, Indiana with pull-down tambour door, pull-out porcelain work surface, and slag glass; 40" wide, 25" deep base, 72" high. Illinois Antique Center. $725.00.*

Plate 26. Seller's kitchen cabinet made in Elwood, Indiana with pull-down tambour door, pull-out porcelain work surface, and slag glass; 48" wide, 28" deep, 70" high. Webb's Antique Mall. $995.00.

Plate 27. Napanee Dutch Kitchenet cabinet made in Nappanee, Indiana with pull-down tambour door and pull-out zinc work surface; 40" wide, 26" deep, 72" high. Private collector. $950.00.

Plate 28. *Hoosier kitchen cabinet made in New Castle, Indiana with Feb. 22, 1910 date on door pulls, pull-out zinc work surface, and frosted design on door panes; 40" wide, 28" deep base, 68" high. Country Shops of Grabill. $895.00.*

Plate 29. *Hoosier type kitchen cabinet with wooden pull-out work surface and roll-out bin at right hand base; 44" wide, 30" deep base, 69" high; Jeffrey's Antique Gallery. $1,250.00.*

Plate 30. *Ariel kitchen cabinet with pull-down tambour door, porcelain pull-out work surface, and built-in New Haven clock; 40" wide, 26" deep base, 70" high; Leo Antique Exchange. $635.00.*

Plate 31. *Hoosier type kitchen cabinet with pull-out zinc work surface, small cabinet and pie shelf on right side base, and frosted design on door panes; 40" wide, 29" deep base, 73" high. Private collector. $1,250.00.*

Plate 32. *Dry sink kitchen cabinet with pull-out wooden work surface supported by a leg; 50" wide, 30" deep base, 77" high. Country Shops of Grabill. $1,950.00.*

Plate 33. Dry sink kitchen cabinet with pull-out work surface supported by a leg on the right hand side; 50" wide, 29" deep, 77" high. Leo Antique Exchange. $2,700.00.

Plate 34. Hawkeye kitchen cabinet made by Union Furniture Co., Burlington, Iowa; 48" wide, 29" deep base, 69" high. Antique America. $1,385.00.

Plate 35. *Dry sink cabinet with swing-out flour bin on the right hand side; 44"
wide, 31" deep base, 71" high. Heartland Antique Mall. $2,250.00*

Chapter Five

Pressed Backs

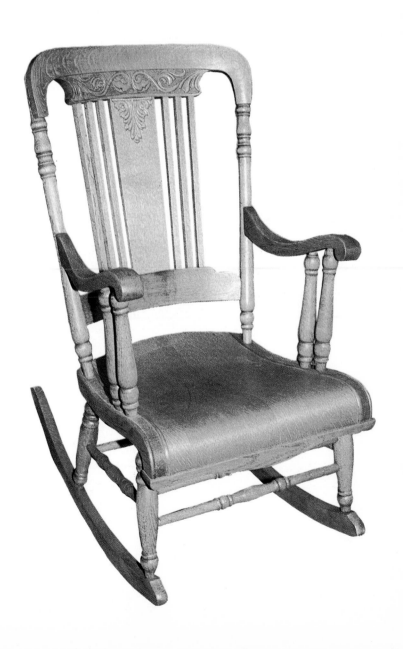

Pressed Backs

When a wooden chair had a design pressed into its back with a metal die or mold, it is called a pressed back chair by contemporary collectors. Steam and strong pressure were combined to create a resemblance to carving.

When chiseling or some hand work was added to the design, the cost increased. Most chairs of this type were oak, but some were fashioned of ash or elm.

The number of pressed designs on an individual chair determines whether the chair is a single, double, triple or quadruple press. On chairs with a single press, it is usually fashioned on the upper slat. When designs are created on other cross pieces, the name changes.

Oftentimes a splat, which is the vertical support in the back of a chair, has a pressed design. The apron under the seat may also be decorated.

Complicated, artistic pressings are of special interest to buyers. For example, embossed male heads with lips formed to blow have been called "Man of the Wind." Floral and geometric designs are found stamped into pressed backs. At times commemorative examples were produced when a facsimile of a famous person's head was stamped onto the top rail or on the splat. Lodge names as well as birds, serpents, medallions, mythological characters and imaginary animal figures have been seen.

Through the examination of furniture sections in old catalogs from the late 1800s to the early 1900s, one can follow the conception and demise of the pressed back chair.

Plate 36. *Pressed-back design on child's high chair. Private collector.*

Plate 37. *Single pressed-back chair;*
37" high. Jeffrey's Antique Gallery.
Four for $750.00.

Plate 38. *Single pressed-back chair; 37" high. Webb's Antique Mall. Five for $600.00.*

Plate 39. *Single pressed-back chair; 36" high. Pleasant Hill Antique Shop. $70.00 each.*

Plate 40. *Single pressed-back chair; 36" high. Antique America.*
$110.00 each.

Plate 41. *Single pressed-back chair; 39" high. Miller's Antique Market. Six for $900.00.*

Plate 42. Single pressed-back chair; 40" high. Jeffrey's Antique Gallery. Four for $500.00.

Plate 43. Single pressed-back chair; 43" high. Jeffrey's Antique Gallery. Four for $945.00.

Plate 44. *Double pressed-back chair; 40" high. Antique America.*
$189.00 each.

Plate 45. *Double pressed-back chair; 42" high. Private collector.*
$155.00 each.

Plate 46. *Triple pressed-back chair; 39" high. Antique America.* $225.00.

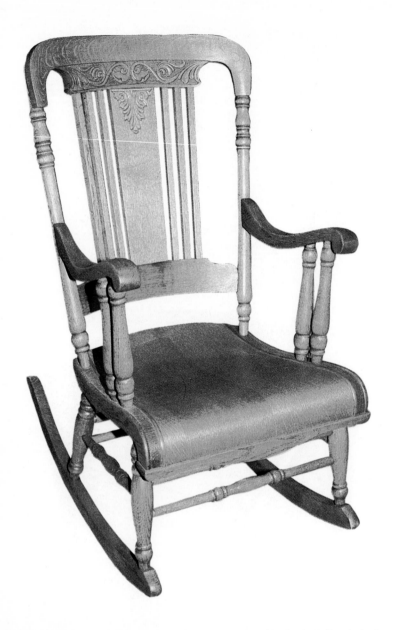

Plate 47. *Single pressed-back rocker; 22" arm to arm, 39" high. Jeffrey's Antique Gallery. $350.00.*

Plate 48. Double pressed-back rocker; 26" arm to arm, 37" high. $235.00.

Plate 49. Double pressed-back rocker; 23" arm to arm, 42" high. Illinois Antique Center. $175.00.

Plate 50. *Double pressed-back rocker; 23" arm to arm, 38" high. Illinois Antique Center. $185.00.*

Chapter Six

Representative Oak Furniture

In the terminating years of the 1800s oak furniture began to replace the darker walnut examples manufactured in the middle and late nineteenth century. Furniture for every room in the house became available in oak or woods with similar characteristics such as ash, chestnut, and elm.

In the general listing that follows, examples of furniture from various parts of the home — kitchen, living room, library, dining room, and bedroom — as well as furniture associated with children, occupations, Stickley, and other mission examples which followed a style similar to his are included in an alphabetical listing.

Each photographic entry includes dimensions, the price as set by its owner and the name of the shop unless the article of furniture is privately owned, and then the phrase "Private Collector" is indicated.

Check back to chapters three, four, and five for an examination of combination bookcase-desks, Hoosier and Hoosier-type kitchen cabinets, and patterns on pressed-back chairs and rockers.

Plate 51. Three piece ash bedroom set with spoon carving; bed, 58" wide; headboard, 69"; footboard, 33"; commode washstand, 30" wide, 16" deep, 76" high; dresser, 40" wide, 18" deep, 75" high. Illinois Antique Center. $2,600.00.

Plate 52. *Ash Murphy bed; 53" wide, 18" deep, 60" high. Private collector. $695.00.*

Plate 53. *Arts and Crafts mission oak bed with leaded glass panel on footboard; headboard 57" wide, 51" high; footboard, 36" high. Antique America. $2,450.00.*

Plate 54. *Double door bookcase with leaded glass upper door panels; 40" wide, 13" deep, 58" high. Illinois Antique Center. $1,000.00.*

Plate 55. *Five piece sectional bookcase with one section reading "Snellenburg & Co., Philadelphia" and the others "Macey;" 34" wide, 12" deep, 70" high. Antique America. $900.00.*

Plate 56. *Three-door bookcase; 60" wide, 13" deep, 62" high. Illinois Antique Center. $1,495.00.*

Plate 57. *Chiffonier (highboy) with swing mirror and bail handles; 32" wide, 19" deep, 66" high. Country Caboose Antiques. $430.00.*

Plate 58. *Chiffonier (highboy) with swing mirror, serpentine top drawer and bail handles; 36" wide, 19" deep, 74" high. Melon City Antique Mart. $825.00.*

Plate 59. *Chiffonier (highboy) with swing mirror, two top Bombay drawers, wooden knobs and paw feet made in Rushville, Indiana by Innis, Pearce & Co.; 44" wide, 22" deep, 70" high. Jeffrey's Antique Gallery. $565.00.*

Plate 60. *Chifforobe with full mirror door; 45" wide, 20" deep, 66" high. Webb's Antique Mall. $499.00.*

Plate 61. Child's roll-top desk; 24" wide, 15" deep, 35" high; Antique America. $165.00.

Plate 62. Child's kindergarten table with two chairs; chairs, 24" high; table, 48" wide, 19" deep, 22" high. Country Shops of Grabill. $325.00.

Plate 63. *Child's doll dresser; 13" wide, 7" deep, 20" high. Miller's Antique Market. $175.00.*

Plate 64. China buffet with swell drawers, applied decorations, paw feet, and grotesques on top of stiles; 48" wide, 20" deep, 60" high. Fifth Street Mall. $1,300.00.

Plate 65. *China buffet with convex glass and pilasters flanking the single center door; 48" wide, 21" deep, 42" high. Private collector. $950.00.*

Plate 66. China cabinet with convex door and side glass panels, round pillars flanking the center door, paw feet, and carved angel head at the top; 46" wide, 14" deep, 73" high. Fifth Street Mall. $3,495.00.

Plate 67. China cabinet with convex door and side glass panels, paw feet, and grotesques near the top; 44" wide, 14" deep, 70" high. Melon City Antique Mart. $2,500.00.

Plate 68. Two-door china cabinet with leaded glass; 39" wide, 14" deep, 64" high. Antique America. $695.00.

Plate 69. Commode with towel bar attachment; 31" wide, 16" deep, 51" high. Jeffrey's Antique Gallery. $485.00.

Plate 70. Commode with towel bar attachment, serpentine drawers and bail handles; 34" wide, 19" deep, 53" high. Country Shops of Grabill. $325.00.

Plate 71. *Commode with towel bar attachment, swing mirror, applied decorations and bail handles; 42" wide, 21" deep, 69" high. Country Shops of Grabill. $595.00.*

Plate 72. Commode with swing top revealing marble top and wash basin, called Princess center table made by Princess Dressing Case Co., Grand Rapids, Michigan, patented Feb. 20, 1883; 36" wide, 24" deep, 31" high. Private collector. $1,200.00.

Plate 73. Two-piece corner cupboard with leaded glass doors; 54" wide, 19" deep, 94" high. Antique America. $2,495.00.

Plate 74. *One-piece straight line cupboard with bail handles and applied decorations; 38" wide, 14" deep, 79" high. Country Shops of Grabill. $825.00.*

Plate 75. Ash stepback cupboard with applied decorations and bail handles; 39" wide, 16" deep, 89" high. Country Shops of Grabill. $995.00.

Plate 76. Stepback cupboard with walnut decorations made by New Bremen Cabinet Company, New Bremen, Ohio; 59" wide, 19" deep, 93" high. Jeffrey's Antique Gallery. $1,850.00.

Plate 77. *Two-piece stepback kitchen cupboard; 40" wide, 17" deep, 74" high. Illinois Antique Center. $950.00.*

Plate 78. *Roll-top desk with applied decorations; 40" wide, 28" deep, 66" high. Fifth Street Mall. $2,850.00.*

Plate 79. *Fall-front desk with Empire-style feet made by Northwestern Cabinet Co., Burlington, Iowa; 32" wide, 12" deep, 64" high. Antique America. $850.00.*

Plate 80. *Fall-front parlor desk with incised decorations; 30" wide, 13" deep, 50" high. Webb's Antique Mall. $395.00.*

Plate 81. Lift-lid student desk; 29" wide, 24" deep, 36" high. Private collector. $445.00.

Plate 82. Cylinder desk with applied decorations, bail handles, and brass railing; 33" wide, 22" deep, 43" high. Illinois Antique Center. $1,095.00.

Plate 83. *Fall-front desk; 28" wide, 11" deep, 66" high. Leo Antique Exchange. $825.00.*

Plate 84. *Round dining table with paw feet and grotesque leg supports; 60" diameter, 30" high. Fifth Street Mall. $5,400.00.*

Plate 85. *Close-up of winged griffin.*

Plate 86. *Round dining table with mission style legs; 54" diameter, 29" high. Melon City Antique Mart. $895.00.*

Plate 87. *Square dining table with paw feet and center support leg; 42" square, 30" high. Melon City Antique Mart. $1,065.00.*

Plate 88. *Dresser with projection top drawers, swing mirror and applied decorations; 44" wide, 22" deep, 73" high. Fifth Street Mall. $485.00.*

Plate 89. *Dresser with swing mirror; 42" wide, 22" deep, 70" high. Melon City Antique Mart. $285.00.*

Plate 90. *Chevalle type dresser with swing mirror, applied decorations, and bail handles; 44" wide, 20" deep, 77" high. Jeffrey's Antique Gallery. $525.00.*

Plate 91. *Sectional file cabinet with 12 drawers in each of the two sections; 27" wide, 16" deep, 37" high. Antique America. $875.00.*

Plate 92. Hall tree with lift-lid storage section and applied decorations; 33" arm to arm, 17" deep, 58" high. Illinois Antique Center. $975.00.

Plate 93. Hall tree with lift-lid storage section, applied decorations and paw feet; 33" arm to arm, 24" deep, 84" high. Webb's Antique Mall. $1,385.00.

Plate 94. Hall tree with lift-lid storage section and applied decorations; 29" arm to arm, 15" deep, 80" high. Karen's Antique Mall. $595.00.

Plate 95. Hall tree with lift-lid storage section, applied decorations, pillasters at each side and paw feet. Fifth Street Mall. $2,695.00.

Plate 96. Hanging drop-lid desk, made by Cortland Desk Co. Lim., Cortland, NY, patented Feb. 8, 1887. Antique America. $650.00.

Plate 97. *Medicine cabinet with "McNernly's" inscribed on upper door frame and "Towel Supply" inscribed on lower; 18" wide, 7" deep, 24" high. Country Caboose Antiques. $195.00.*

Plate 98. *Ice box; 37" wide, 21" deep, 43" high. Antique America. $525.00.*

Plate 99. *Ice box made in Muncie, IN; 36" wide, 22" deep, 55" high. Country Shops of Grabill. $510.00.*

Plate 100. *Lady's fall-front desk with grotesques above front legs, bowed drawer, claw and ball feet, and removable legs; 28" wide, 16" deep, 41" high. Country Caboose Antiques. $495.00.*

Plate 101. *Lady's fall-front desk with applied decorations and cabriole legs; 30" wide, 15" deep, 46" high. Fifth Street Mall. $695.00.*

Plate 102. *Lady's fall-front desk with incised decorations; 27" wide, 17" deep, 56" high. Leo Antique Exchange. $675.00.*

Plate 103. Library table with twist legs; 44" wide, 28" deep, 29" high, with accompanying chair that is not pictured. Illinois Antique Center. $795.00.

Plate 104. Library table with incised carving on door. Attached label reads "Factory #16, Larkin Co., Buffalo, N.Y.;" 36" wide, 24" deep, 29" high. Leo Antique Exchange. $320.00.

Plate 105. *Library table with bookshelf sides; 39" wide, 25" deep, 29" high. Karen's Antique Mall. $335.00.*

Plate 106. *Dental cabinet with applied decorations, pull-out tray, and four full-width serpentine drawers; 26" wide, 16" deep, 66" high. Fifth Street Mall. $3,995.00.*

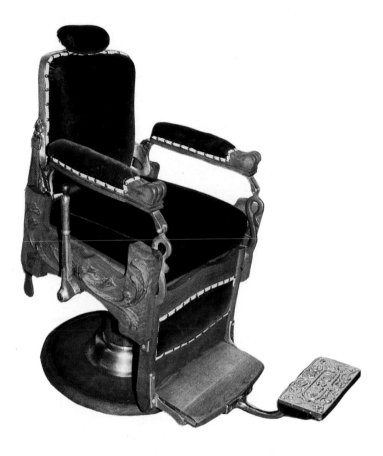

Plate 107. *Barber's chair marked "Koken Hydraulic Barber's Chair"*
with applied designs on wooden base, maroon upholstery, and "Kochs"
marked on foot rest; 23" arm to arm, 43" high. Illinois Antique Center.
$1,350.00.

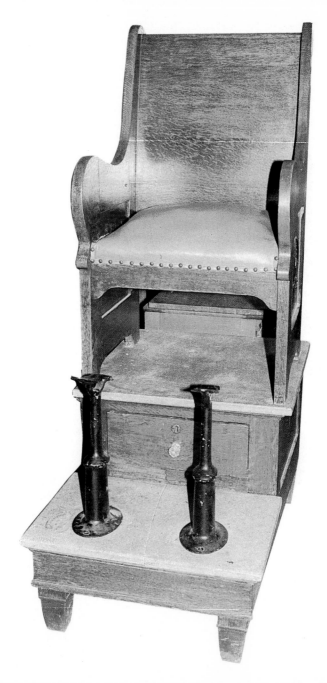

Plate 108. *Shoe shine stand with metal shoe holders on marble slab; 26" wide, 41" deep, 65" high. Jeffrey's Antique Gallery. $525.00.*

Plate 109. Draftsman's swivel stool; 16" diameter seat, 43" high. Heartland Antique Mall. Set of four, $725.00.

Plate 110. Parlor table with metal decorations at top of legs; 16" square, 27" high. Illinois Antique Center. $185.00.

Plate 111. *Parlor table with ball designs on apron and legs; 18" square, 29" high. Illinois Antique Center. $165.00.*

Plate 112. *Parlor table with claw and ball feet; 28" square, 30" high. Country Shops of Grabill. $450.00.*

Plate 113. *Lakeside roller-type phonograph with 70 cylinders; 13" wide, 18" deep, 14" high. Private collector. $350.00.*

Plate 114. *Victrola phonograph that was featured in the Bix film; 20" wide, 22" deep, 43" high. $400.00.*

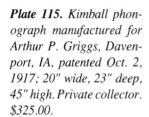

Plate 115. Kimball phonograph manufactured for Arthur P. Griggs, Davenport, IA, patented Oct. 2, 1917; 20" wide, 23" deep, 45" high. Private collector. $325.00.

Plate 116. Close-up of trademark on Kimball phonograph.

Plate 117. Pedestal; 13" diameter, 35" high. Jeffrey's Antique Gallery. $225.00.

Plate 118. *Princess dresser with swing mirror and serpentine drawers; 39" wide, 21" deep, 70" high. Illinois Antique Center. $310.00.*

Plate 119. *Princess dresser with swing mirror, serpentine drawers, and cabriole legs; 34" wide, 20" deep, 72" high. Jeffrey's Antique Gallery. $425.00.*

Plate 120. *Princess dresser with swing mirror, serpentine drawers, and applied decorations; 38" wide, 21" deep, 76" high. Melon City Antique Mart. $575.00.*

Plate 121. Quarter-sawed oak arm rocker; 26" arm to arm, 37" high. American Country Antiques. $450.00.

Plate 122. Platform rocker with applied and incised decorations and brass trim; 25" arm to arm, 35" high. Private collector. $495.00.

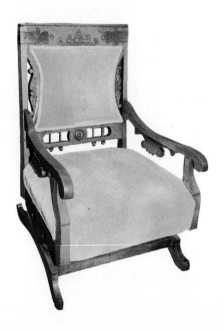

Plate 123. *Low-arm rocker; 22" arm to arm, 45" high. Jeffrey's Antique Gallery. $255.00.*

Plate 124. *Buffet or server with paneled doors and bail handles; 45" wide, 23" deep, 59" high. Melon City Antique Mart. $795.00.*

Plate 125. *Sideboard with applied and incised decorations and two serpentine drawers; 45" wide, 21" deep, 79" high. Private collector. $1,695.00.*

Plate 126. *Buffet with top swell drawers and "Empire" style scroll legs; 54" wide, 23" deep, 56" high. Jeffrey's Antique Gallery. $595.00.*

Plate 127. *Sideboard server with two serpentine drawers, cabriole legs, and paw feet; 43" wide, 20" deep, 63" high. Leo Antique Exchange. $565.00.*

*Plate 128. Uphol-
stered love seat with
tufted back and in-
cised decorations; 35"
wide, 22" deep, 36"
high. Illinois Antique
Center. $275.00.*

*Plate 129. Upholstered sofa with attached end tables and applied and incised
decorations; 78" wide, 27" deep, 45" high. Private collector. $1,900.00.*

Plate 130. *Gustav Stickley bookcase, 42" wide, 13" deep, 56" high. Private collector. $3,500.00.*

Plate 131. *Gustav Stickley's "Als Ik Kan" label found on the pictured bookcase.*

Plate 132. *Taboret with pressed designs; 20" across top, 31" high. Pleasant Hill Antique Shop. $395.00.*

Plate 133. Umbrella stand with brass pan in base; 12" diameter, 26" high. Hickory Hill Antiques. $135.00.

Plate 134. Umbrella stand with metal pan in base; 11" square, 28" high. Private collector. $225.00.

Plate 135. *Vanity or dressing table with swing mirror, applied decorations, serpentine drawers, and cabriole legs; 39" wide, 23" deep, 73" high. Fifth Street Mall. $895.00.*

Plate 136. *Vanity or dressing table with swing mirror, swell top drawers, and cabriole legs; 38" wide, 21" deep, 72" high. Fifth Street Mall. $485.00.*

Plate 137. *Vanity or dressing table with swing side mirrors and Empire scroll legs advertised in early twentieth century catalogues as "Colonial Style;" 38" wide, 21" deep, 60" high. Antique America. $395.00.*

Plate 138. Wardrobe with applied decorations on the cornice; 40" wide, 16" deep, 87" high. Country Shops of Grabill. $895.00.

Plate 139. Wardrobe with darkly grained center panels; 45" wide, 18" deep, 85" high. Country Shops of Grabill. $795.00.

Plate 140. Wardrobe with applied decorations and highly figured door panels; 51" wide, 18" deep, 84" high. Country Caboose Antiques. $1,295.00.

Schroeder's
ANTIQUES
Price Guide . . . is the #1 best-selling

antiques & collectibles value guide on the market today,
and here's why . . .

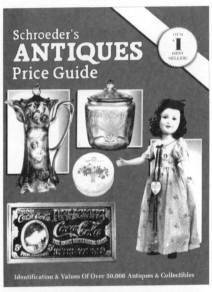

Schroeder's
ANTIQUES
Price Guide

OUR #1 BEST SELLER!

Identification & Values Of Over 50,000 Antiques & Collectibles

8½ X 11 • 608 Pgs. • PB • $12.95